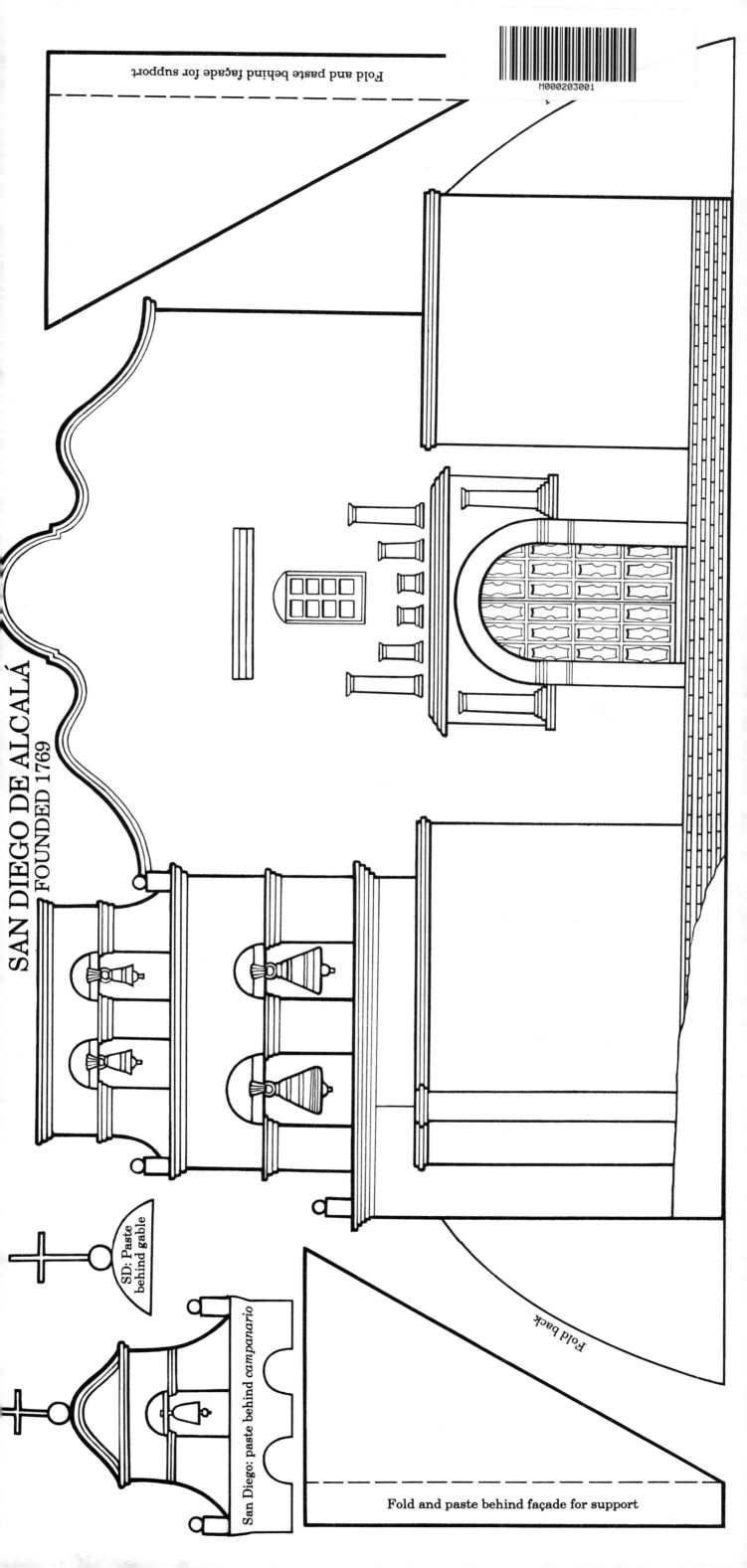

SAN DIEGO DE ALCALÁ
FOUNDED 1769

Fold and paste behind façade for support

Fold back

Fold and paste behind façade for support

SD: Paste behind gable

San Diego: paste behind *campanario*

M000203001

SAN DIEGO DE ALCALÁ

California's first mission, dedicated to San Diego de Alcalá (Saint Didacus of Alcalá) was founded on July 16, 1769 on a hill overlooking San Diego Bay; for its first five years it shared a stockade with the presidio. In 1774 it was decided that the mission would be better off at a site separate from the military. Accordingly the site was moved upstream about five miles, and a small church was put up only to be burned in the Indian uprising of 1775.

Two more churches occupied the site before work began on the final one in 1807. Built of adobe with a brick façade, the church, as reconstructed in 1930, was 48 *varas* long and 9⅓ *varas* wide. By 1810 a flat roof was competed, but the next year it had to be replaced and the upper part of the façade rebuilt because cracks began to appear. This was surely due to the placement of the front of the church right on the edge of the hill. It is likely that the two enormous triangular buttresses were added to the façade at this point. They were what probably saved the church from major damage in the 1812 earthquake so that it could be blessed in November the following year.

As originally designed the church had architectural ornament around the doorway with a small niche beneath the choir window. These features echo details common in 16th century churches in Mexico, while the undulating outline of the gable is more typical of the baroque style of the 17th and 18th centuries; both styles were old-fashioned by the time this mission church was built. The bell-wall or *espadaña* with three levels of bells has a long history in Hispanic architecture. At an unknown date a triple-arched portico was built between the buttresses. It had a tile roof, and this effectively destroyed the ornament above the cornice on top of the door; the niche was filled in, and the choir window was enlarged.

The mission was secularized in 1834, and the decay of the buildings began. In the early 1850s the mission buildings were occupied by the United States Army and extensively modified. By the end of the century little more remained than the façade with its huge buttresses, fragments of the side walls and one room of the front wing. Around 1900 the California Landmarks Club stabilized the walls, and a bit of rebuilding of the side walls began in 1920. Finally a complete rebuilding of the church, in modern materials, was carried out in 1929-30.

Symbols of San Diego de Alcalá

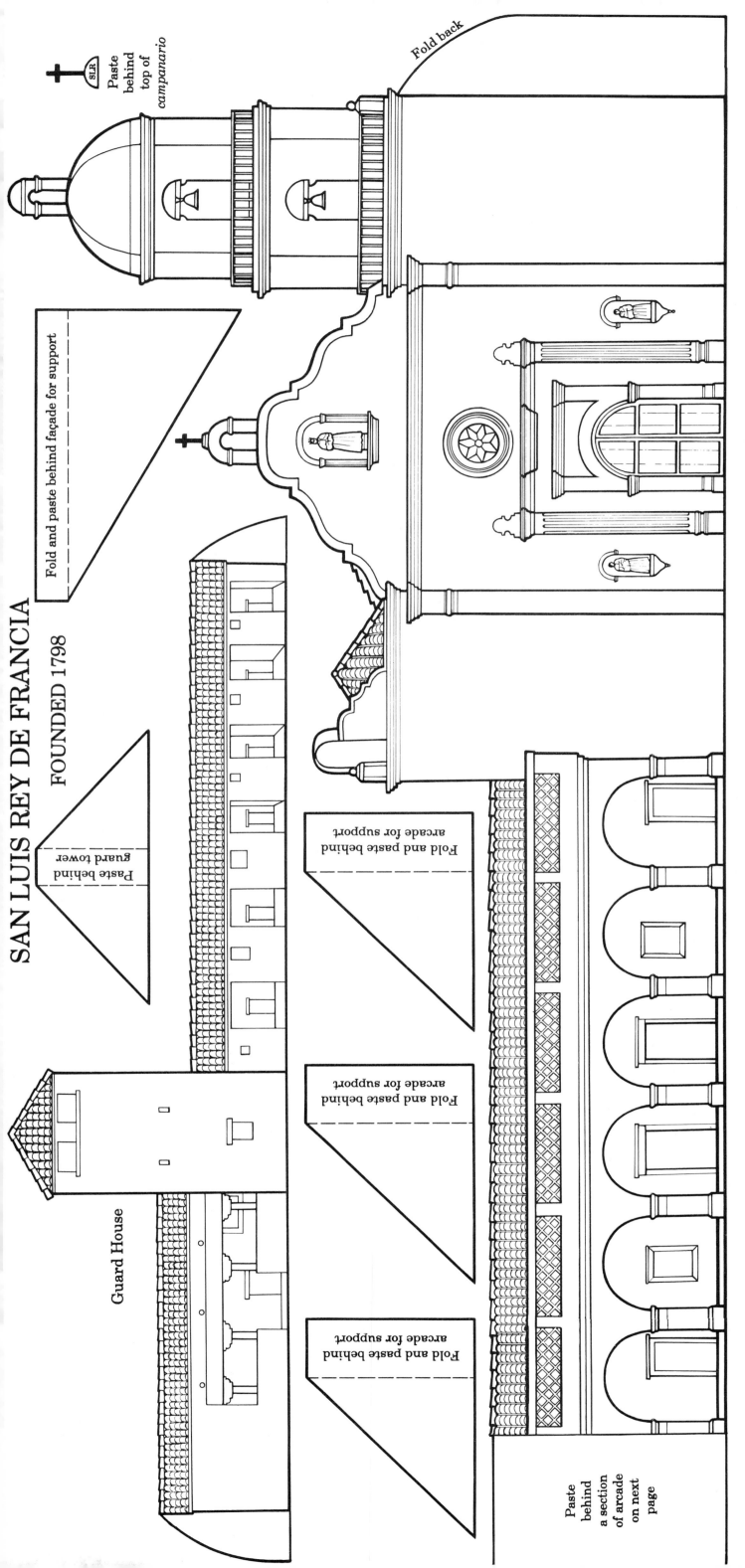

SAN LUIS REY DE FRANCIA
FOUNDED 1798

Paste behind top of *campanario*

SLR

Fold back

Fold and paste behind façade for support

Paste behind guard tower

Guard House

Fold and paste behind arcade for support

Fold and paste behind arcade for support

Fold and paste behind arcade for support

Paste behind a section of arcade on next page

SAN LUIS REY DE FRANCIA

The eighteenth of the California missions, dedicated to San Luis Rey de Francia (Saint Louis King of France) was founded on June 13, 1798. It was the last of a group of five missions founded by Fr. Fermín Francisco de Lasuén to fill in major gaps in the coastal chain. San Luis Rey become the largest and most populous Indian mission (2869 in 1826) not only in California but in both Americas.

A first adobe church with a flat roof was built soon after the founding, but in 1802 a new one with a tiled roof was built. Over the next few years many parts of the quadrangle were built. In 1811 the foundation trenches for the present church were opened, and on October 4th the cornerstone was placed. The document which records this gives the name of the architect and master of the works as José Antonio Ramírez. This is the only documented instance of anyone being called "architect" for a California mission. He was a Spaniard born in the state of Jalisco in Mexico, and came to California as a master carpenter in 1792.

The plan of the church is that of a Latin cross. It is one of only two with this plan in California; the other was at neighboring San Juan Capistrano where Ramírez had worked a few years before. He would have known that church and may have chosen to emulate that design, the most ambitious in California. That church was of stone, but San Luis Rey's is of adobe with the tower and façade of brick. Nothing is known of the stone church's façade, so we cannot say if it influenced San Luis Rey's rather unusual design. Two plain pilasters frame the façade. The entrance door has an arch integrated into a rectangular frame. This, in turn, is framed by two pilasters and an entablature echoing the frame of the façade. This unique feature suggests a projecting vestibule pushed back into the façade. The

The Guard House, San Luis Rey De Francia

It was customary for each mission to have a structure to house the small detachment of soldiers assigned there as protection against hostile Indians and possible invaders. Our view is from an 1850 drawing by Cave Couts and shows the lookout tower and living quarters for the soldiers.

Arms of
San Luis Rey

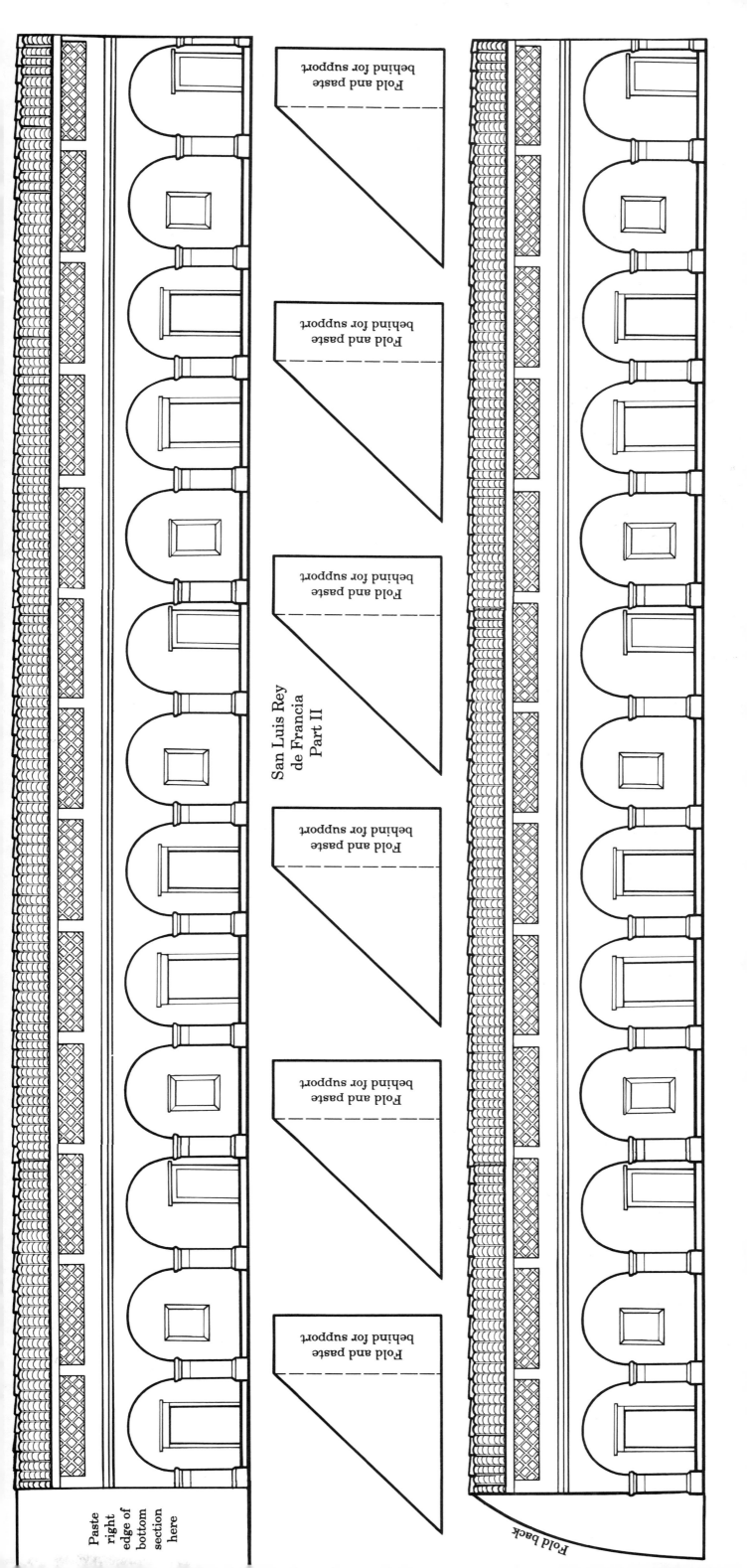

San Luis Rey
de Francia
Part II

Fold and paste behind for support

Fold and paste behind for support

Fold and paste behind for support

Fold and paste behind for support

Fold and paste behind for support

Fold and paste behind for support

Paste right edge of bottom section here

Fold back

Fold back

circular choir window above is one of only two known in the California missions (the other is at Santa Bárbara). The gable with its undulating outline is the most complex in California. The niche in the center once contained a figure of Saint Louis of France while the two niches flanking the door had statues of saints Dominic and Francis, echoing the arrangement of the images on the main altar within the church. The little arch on top of the gable acts as a pedestal for the cross and echoes the lantern on top of the dome of the adjoining belltower.

Originally two belltowers must have been planned but only one was actually constructed. The part flanking the façade of the completed one contained a stairway giving access to the bell chambers while the other one contained the baptistry. A room above, accessible from an outside stair behind, gave onto the choir loft. With the cut-off corners the two bell chambers were octagonal in plan. There were originally exterior railings of wood on both levels; the lower one had masonry corner posts on the cemetery side. These were repeated on the unfinished tower on the side toward the courtyard. The structure suggesting a corner of a bell chamber is finished off in an undulating slope, echoing the form of the gable.

The walls of the church had reached the cornice level in 1812, and the following year the front wing of the patio with its arcade was finished, while work on the arcade inside the patio was half done. The church was completed and blessed in 1815, four years to the day after the cornerstone was laid. In 1829 four brick arches at the crossing were built to hold a wooden hemispherical dome. Its only indication on the exterior was a cupola or lantern with eight columns holding up a pointed dome; there were windows formed of 144 panes of glass between the columns. It is probable that at that time the ceilings and inside of the dome were covered with flat boards and cloth glued to them with painted ornament to suggest a plastered ceiling.

A door on the west gave access to a small garden court, a unique feature in the planning of the mission. It appears to have been a flower garden for the church. On the exterior there was an elaborate frame, repeating the central motif of the façade, with a framed niche above. It had a painted design inside. On the cemetery side of the church a door opened onto an octagonal, domed chapel with a projecting altar area with its own small dome. The documents refer to it as the chapel of Saint Francis, and it originally had no access from the cemetery as it does now. It does not appear to have been a mortuary chapel as these were not customary in California.

As no town grew up around the mission it was soon abandoned and looted, especially for building materials, though the church continued to be used for services from time to time. Eventually the dome and parts of the roof began to collapse, and the crossing and chancel were closed off while the nave continued to be used for Mass. In 1892 Mexican Franciscans from Zacatecas began to occupy the mission and initiated the rebuilding and restoration which still continues.

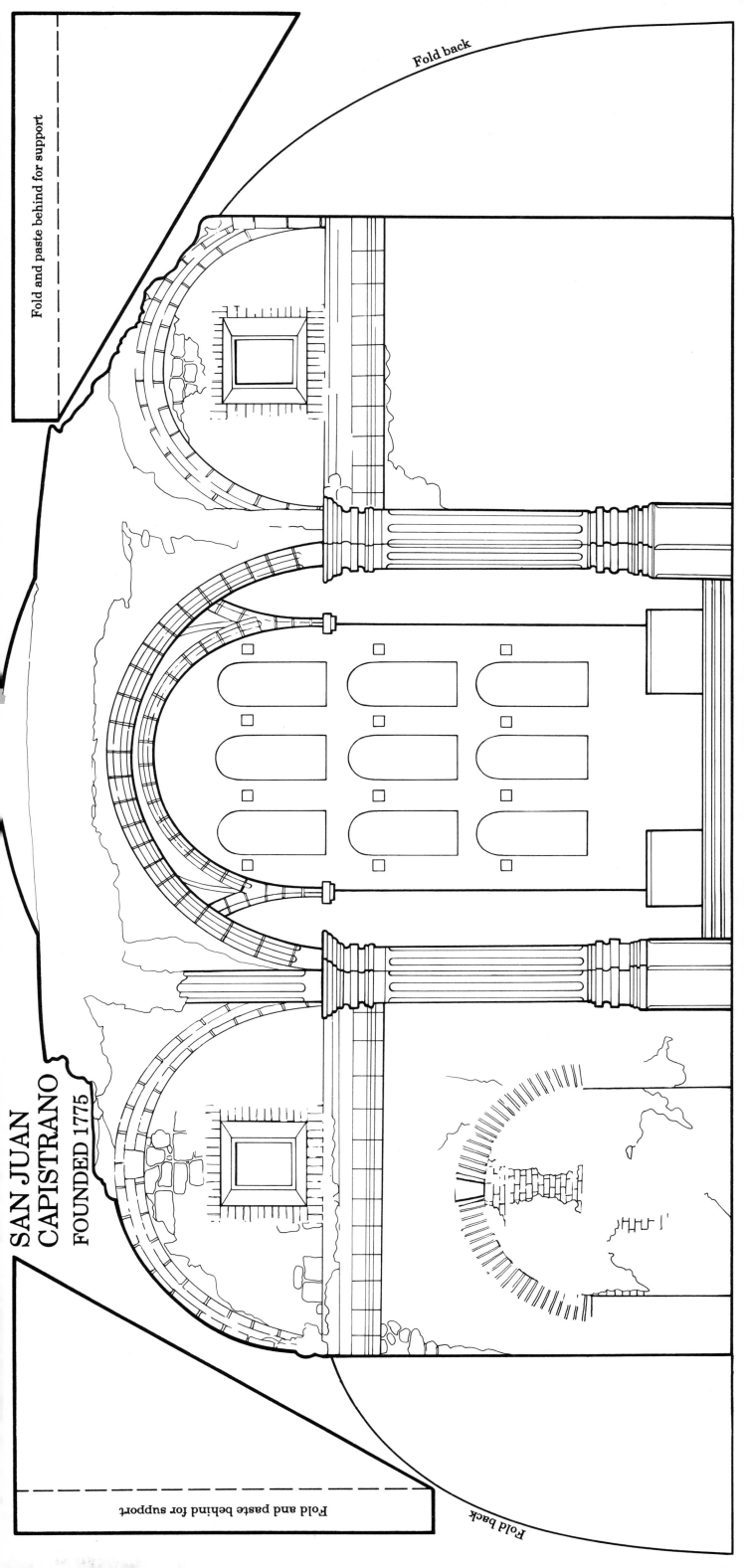

SAN JUAN
CAPISTRANO
FOUNDED 1775

Fold back

Fold and paste behind for support

Fold and paste behind for support

Fold back

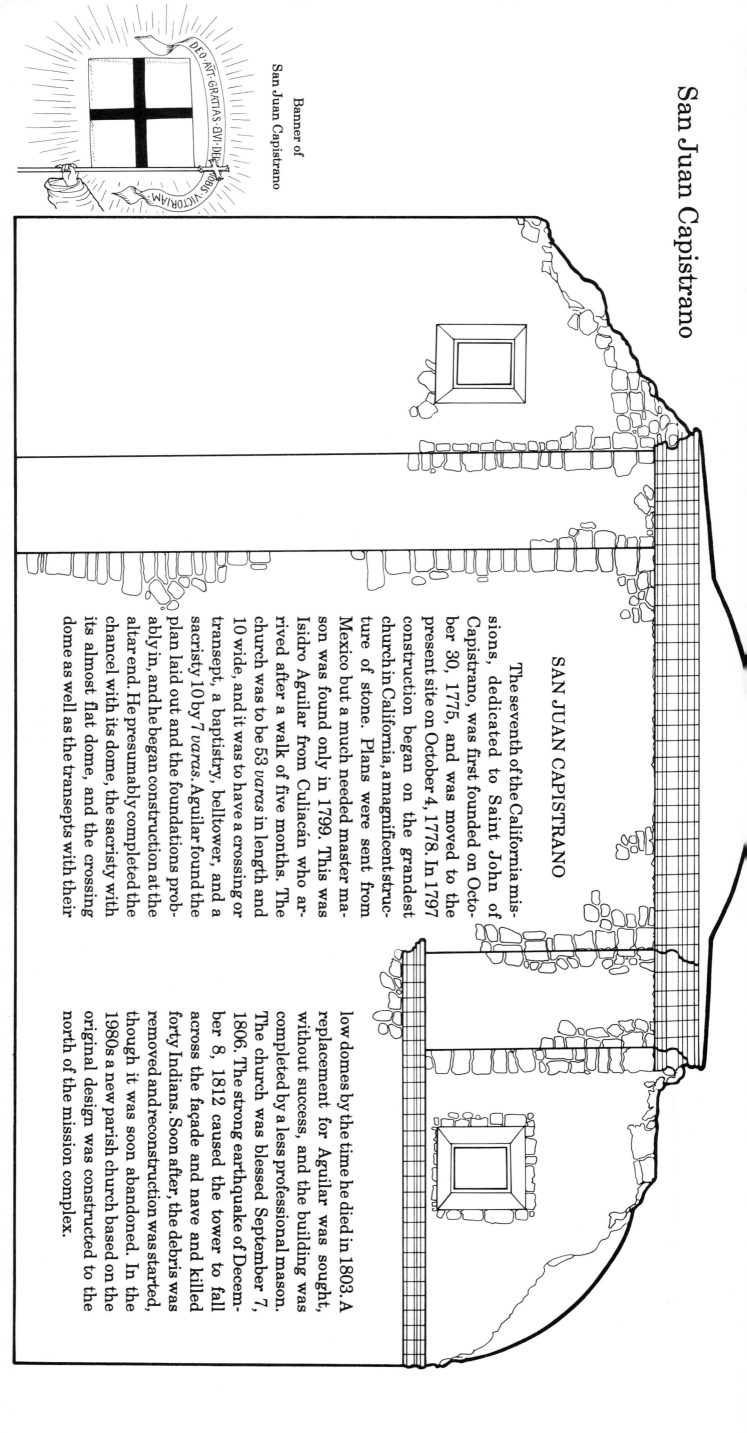

Banner of
San Juan Capistrano

DEO·AIT·GRATIAS·ĞVI·DEDIT·NOBIS·VICTORIAM

SAN JUAN CAPISTRANO

The seventh of the California missions, dedicated to Saint John of Capistrano, was first founded on October 30, 1775, and was moved to the present site on October 4, 1778. In 1797 construction began on the grandest church in California, a magnificent structure of stone. Plans were sent from Mexico but a much needed master mason was found only in 1799. This was Isidro Aguilar from Culiacán who arrived after a walk of five months. The church was to be 53 *varas* in length and 10 wide, and it was to have a crossing or transept, a baptistry, belltower, and a sacristy 10 by 7 *varas*. Aguilar found the plan laid out and the foundations probably in, and he began construction at the altar end. He presumably completed the chancel with its dome, the sacristy with its almost flat dome, and the crossing dome as well as the transepts with their

low domes by the time he died in 1803. A replacement for Aguilar was sought, without success, and the building was completed by a less professional mason. The church was blessed September 7, 1806. The strong earthquake of December 8, 1812 caused the tower to fall across the façade and nave and killed forty Indians. Soon after, the debris was removed and reconstruction was started, though it was soon abandoned. In the 1980s a new parish church was constructed to the original design based on the north of the mission complex.

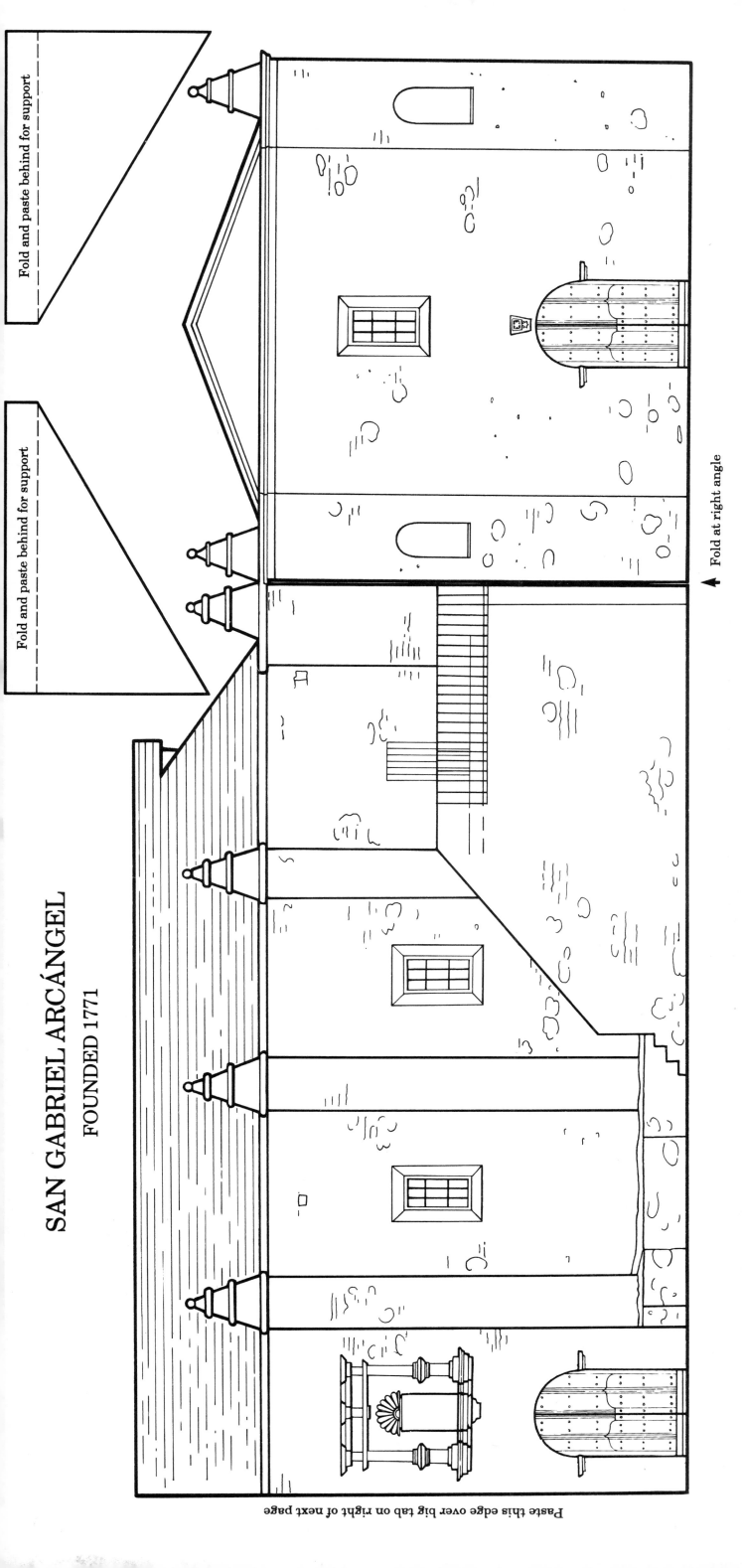

SAN GABRIEL ARCÁNGEL
FOUNDED 1771

Fold and paste behind for support

Fold and paste behind for support

Fold at right angle

Paste this edge over big tab on right of next page

SAN GABRIEL ARCÁNGEL

Mission San Gabriel Arcángel was founded on September 4, 1771, about five miles from its present location near the Río del Nombre de Jesús de los Temblores (River of the Name of Jesus of the Earthquakes), known today as the Santa Ana River. The first chapel was built of reeds and was about four by twelve *varas*. A larger chapel, six by fifteen *varas*, built of vertical posts with a thatched roof, replaced this in 1773. In 1775, however, the mission was moved to the present site because of frequent floods which ruined the crops. The next year the first adobe church, seven by thirty-six *varas*, was built to the north of the cemetery. It had a door on the façade, six windows, and a flat roof; there was a sacristy five *varas* square which had a window and a door to the patio. Sometime in the 1780s a tile roof was put on the church.

The present church was begun about 1790 in stone and brick; it was one of several stone churches in California. As first built, the church was vaulted and had a single nave with a choir loft over the entrance with the sanctuary at the opposite end and the sacristy behind. North of the main entrance was the *campanario* with arches in a flat wall, the sort called an *espadaña*. A room in the lower part contained the stairs to the choir loft, while a domed baptistry projected into the cemetery. The side walls are each divided into nine bays by ten buttresses. Those on the north, or cemetery, side stop a few feet below the top of the wall while those on the south side are full height and are topped by pyramids which once held stone balls. These buttresses served to support cross arches to separate the vaults and to counteract the thrust of the weight of the roof. This scheme is modeled on Mexican examples, such as ones placed on the corner of a city block.

San Gabriel Arcángel
Part II

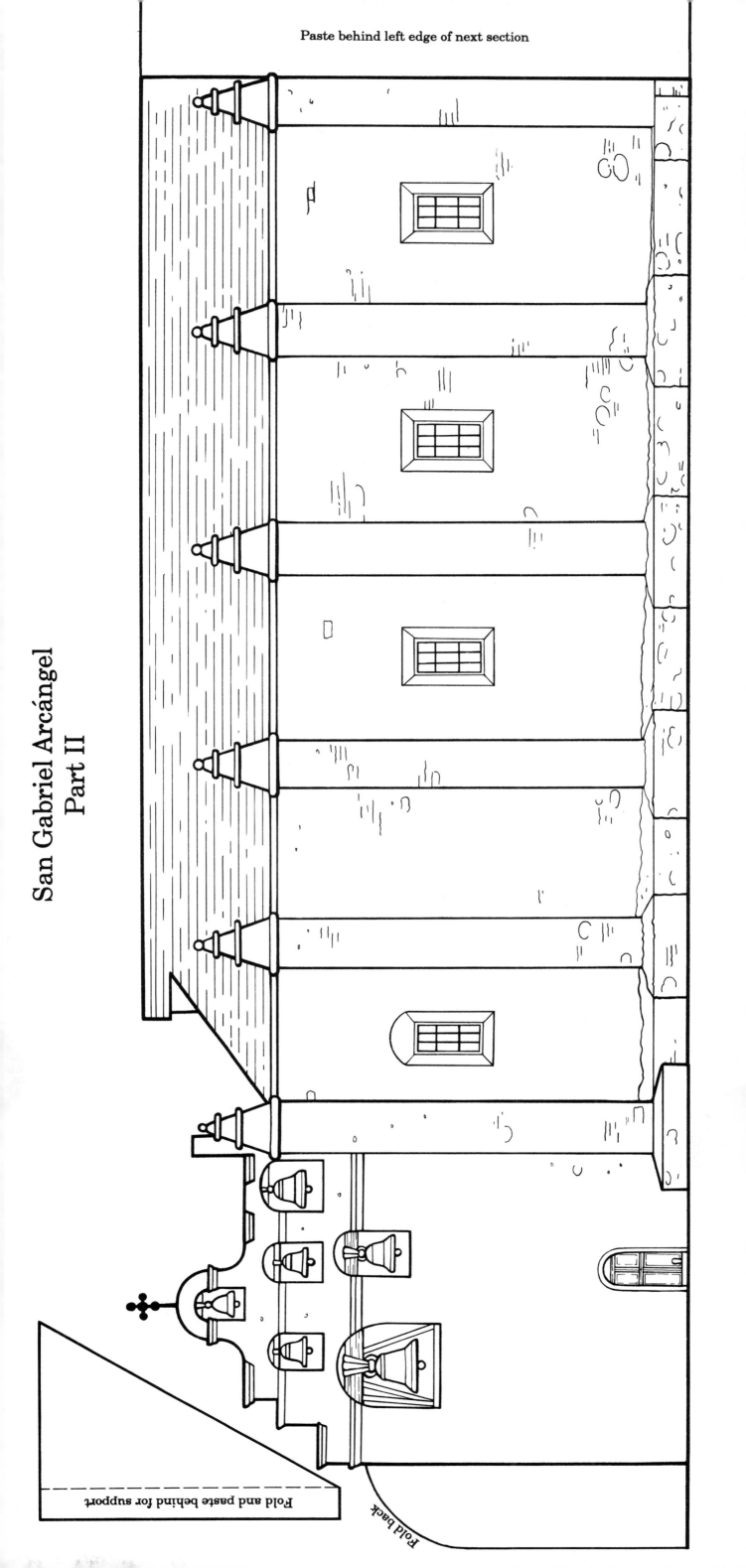

Fold back

A side door had a decorative niche above on the south side while a door on the north wall gave access to the cemetery. A low parapet wall topped the sacristy between the church and the fathers' dwelling, which continued on the same axis, though mission churches are usually perpendicular to the front wing and form one side of the quadrangle. The church was already half-done in 1793, and by 1797 all but one of the vaults was completed. The church was roofed with a series of domes or vaults of stone and mortar, but cracks already began to appear in 1801. Worse ones appeared after an earthquake in 1803 when the church had already been blessed. A skilled mason recommended taking the vaults down, but that was not done until 1808 when a flatter roof covered with floor tiles replaced them.

In 1812 the church was seriously damaged in another earthquake. The *campanario* collapsed. It was not repaired, and the bells were then transferred to a new *espadaña* built on top of the sacristy parapet wall. At that point there were five bells, placed symmetrically on three levels. Another bell, cast in 1830, was acquired, and the lower left-hand arch was enlarged to accommodate it, while a third arch was added on the right of the middle level for the displaced bell. At some point, not recorded, a new hipped roof, covered with tile, replaced the flat roof. It had a cupola on the end above the altar to supply light from above. A new, outside stairway, next to the façade, now gave access to the choir. In 1865 the decayed roof was replaced by one covered with shingles rather than tiles, and the cupola was removed. In 1886 a totally new roof was installed and the windows were lengthened downward.

Symbols of San Gabriel

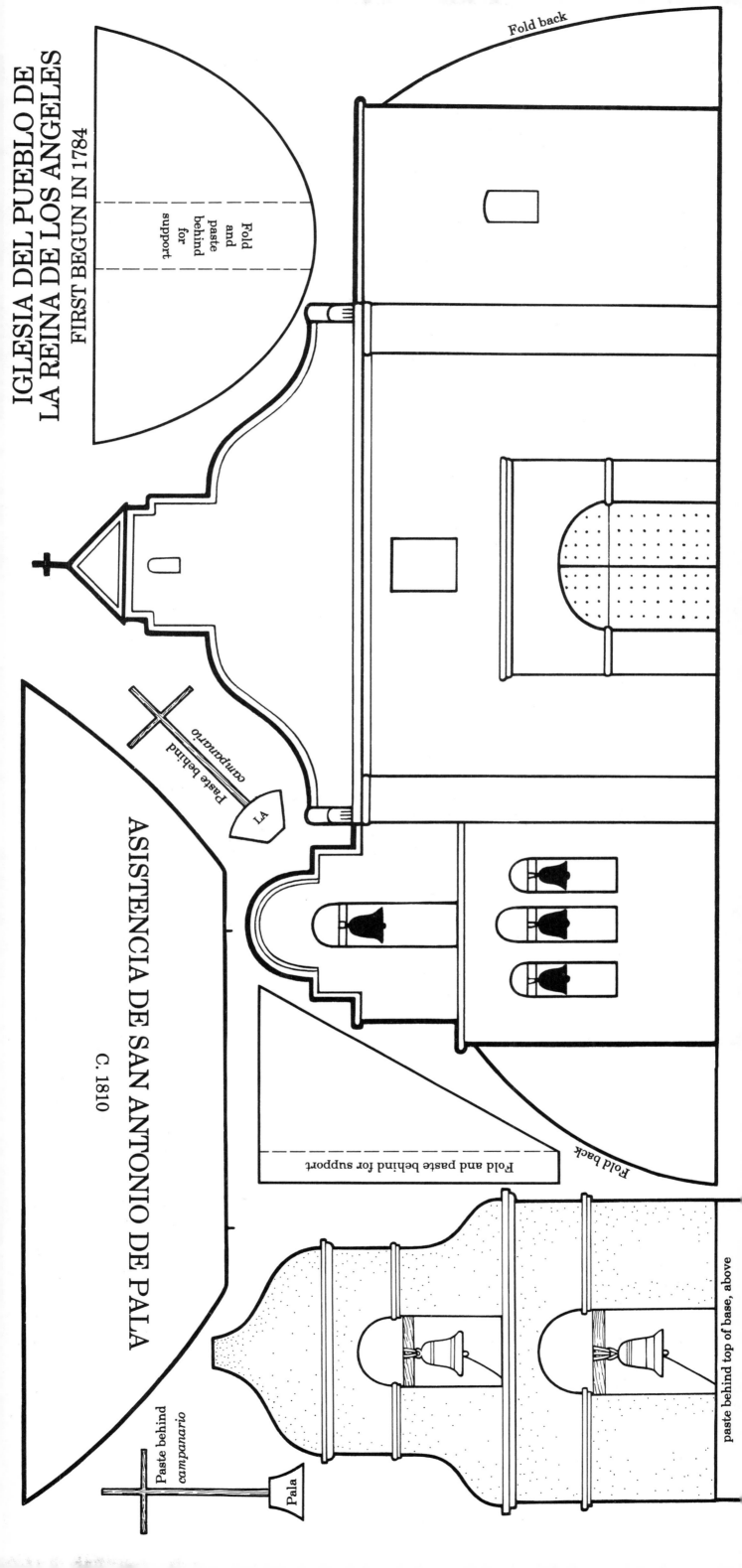

IGLESIA DEL PUEBLO DE LA REINA DE LOS ANGELES

FIRST BEGUN IN 1784

Fold and paste behind for support

Fold back

Fold back

Paste behind campanario

LA

ASISTENCIA DE SAN ANTONIO DE PALA

C. 1810

Fold and paste behind for support

Fold back

Paste behind campanario

Pala

paste behind top of base, above

IGLESIA DEL PUEBLO DE LA REINA DE LOS ANGELES

The city of La Reina de los Angeles was founded on September 4, 1781. No church was located on the first plan of the pueblo, but one was begun in 1784 and finished in 1789-90. The structure soon proved inadequate and a new church was begun in 1815, but before the end of the year the site was inundated by the Los Angeles River (Río de Porciúncula) and was abandoned. The present site was selected not far from the first one. The church was designed by José Antonio Ramírez, who had been the architect of the church of Mission San Luis Rey. He worked on the church from 1820 to 1822, when it was finally dedicated, and was buried there upon his death in 1827. The church, cruciform in plan, was 27 feet wide and 135 feet long (90 feet to the crossing). Originally

the church had a tile roof, but by 1847 a flat roof covered with *brea* (tar) had replaced it. An *espadaña* to the left of the façade held the bells on two levels: three arches on the lower level and a single one above; a short distance behind it stood the baptistry. The façade is reminiscent of Ramírez's design at San Luis Rey, with flat pilasters at the sides connected by a cornice, an arched doorway within a rectangular frame, and an undulating gable with a projecting element above.

In 1860 heavy rains caused the upper part of the façade to weaken and fall, and a new façade, the present one, took its place. The mission-style *espadaña* standing today dates from 1913, and in appearance suggests little of the original one.

ASISTENCIA OF SAN ANTONIO DE PALA

What became the *asistencia* or sub-mission of San Antonio de Pala began as an outlying rancho of Mission San Luis Rey. The earliest surviving mention of it is in that mission's annual report of 1810.

The chapel is long and narrow, 107 by 19½ feet inside with a sacristy behind. There is no façade as such, though a porch of four adobe pillars shelters the entrance and one room to the left.

Near the front wall of the cemetery is a singular, free-standing campanile of brick on a cobblestone base, once plastered. The feature of two superimposed arches topped by a graceful gable is unique among mission belfries, though it belongs in the tradition of *espadañas*.

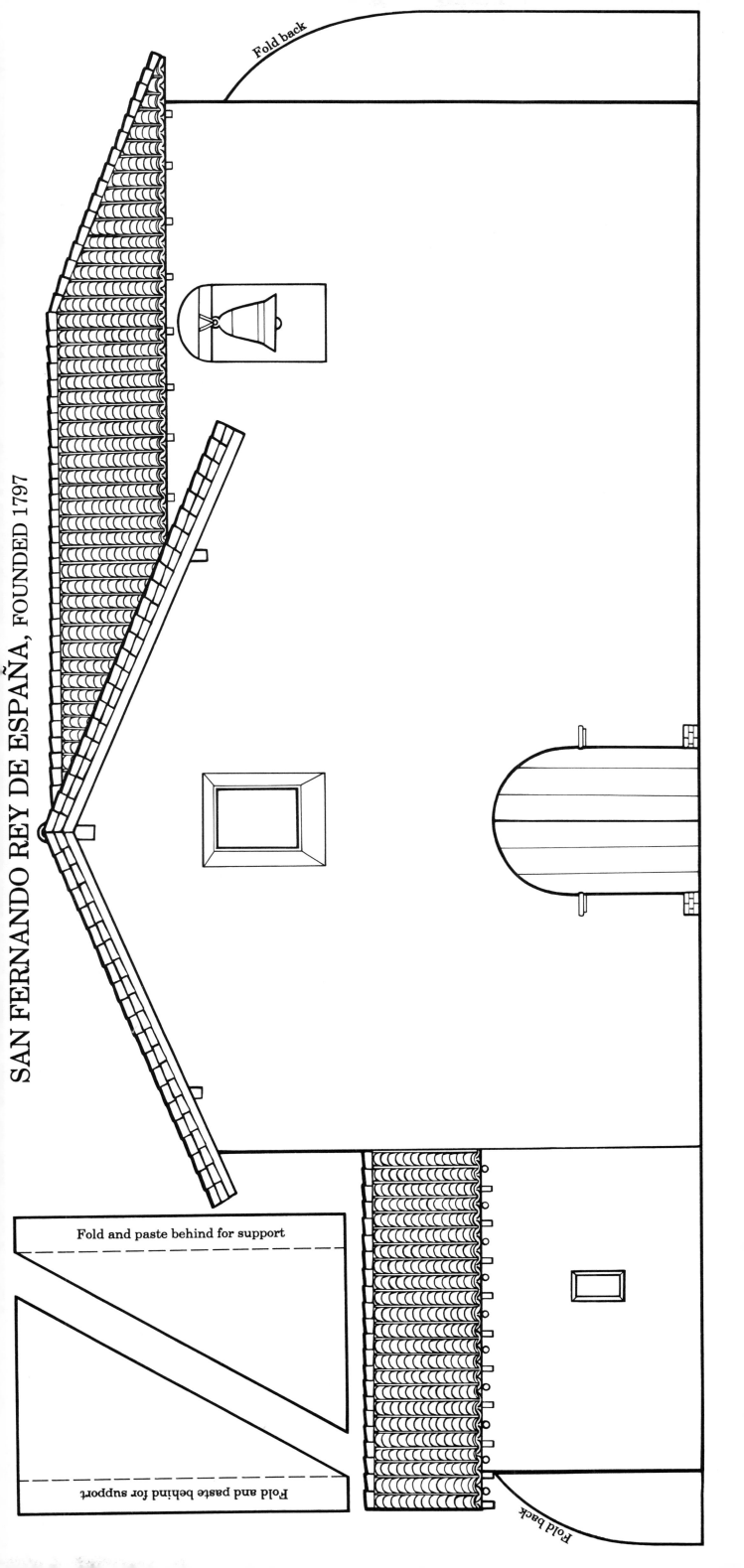

SAN FERNANDO REY DE ESPAÑA, FOUNDED 1797

Fold back

Fold back

Fold and paste behind for support

Fold and paste behind for support

Fold back

SAN FERNANDO REY DE ESPAÑA

The seventeenth of the California missions, dedicated to San Fernando Rey de España (Saint Ferdinand King of Spain) was founded September 8, 1797, as the fourth of five missions founded to fill major gaps in the coastal chain. The first church, an adobe structure 8 *varas* long, was completed and blessed on December 6, 1806. We are lacking information as to when it was begun or any details concerning it. The church suffered some damage in the 1812 earthquake. The exterior was plain in the extreme with only an arched entrance doorway with a rectangular window above for the façade. However, it may at one time have had painted ornament like the church at Santa Clara since the later fathers' dwelling was extensively decorated on its front. The bells were hung in the upper chamber of a structure to the right which rose to the height of the church's walls. The interior was elaborately articulated with pilasters along the side walls with arched recesses in between, a feature found elsewhere only in the stone church at San Juan Capistrano in a more complex manner.

As originally laid out, the church formed one side of a quadrangle with the fathers' dwelling next to the *campanario* with a corridor for part of its length with brick pillars. All of these were square except for two flanking the door to the *sala*. In 1810 a separate and much grander fathers' dwelling was begun and completed in 1822 with a handsome arcade. It went through various phases before reaching the final form. It may have been conceived of as the beginning of a new quadrangle with a grander church, though all that remained nothing more than a fond dream.

The church remained serviceable into the 1870s, but once the roof began to fall in and the tiles were removed it deteriorated rapidly. It received a temporary roof in 1897 due to efforts of the California Landmarks Club, but that proved inadequate and deterioration continued. Efforts toward repair and restoration increased in the 1930s and climaxed in the rededication in 1941, though the *campanario* and sacristy were completed only after the end of World War II. Unfortunately the church was seriously damaged in the 1971 earthquake and was demolished to be replaced by a replica in modern materials.

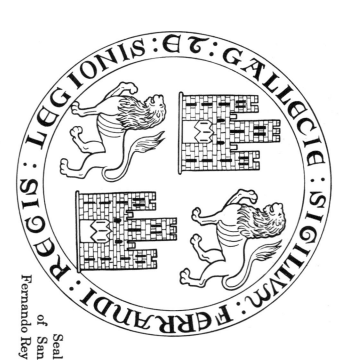

Seal of San Fernando Rey

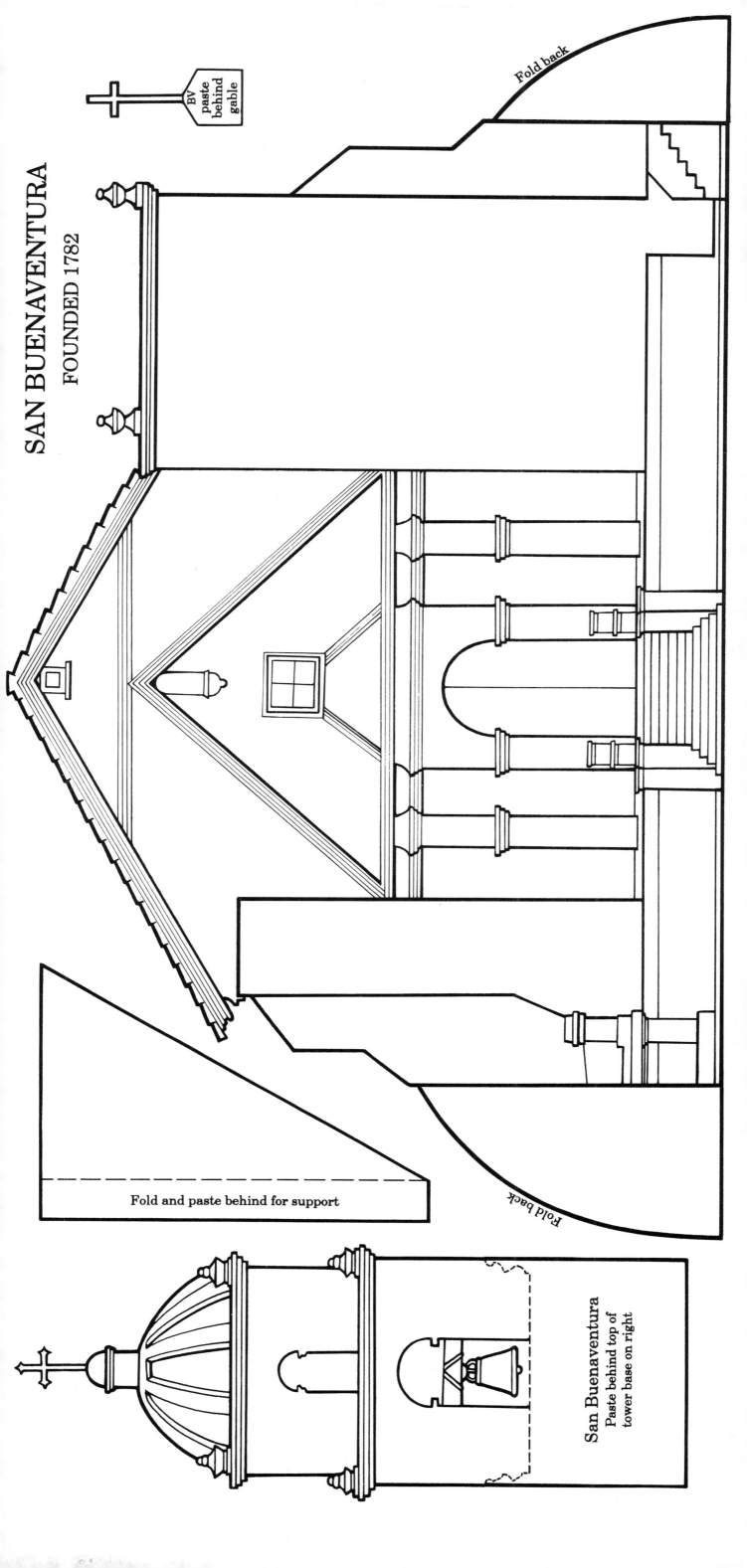

SAN BUENAVENTURA
FOUNDED 1782

BV paste behind gable

Fold back

Fold back

Fold and paste behind for support

San Buenaventura
Paste behind top of
tower base on right

SAN BUENAVENTURA

The ninth mission, dedicated to San Buenaventura (Saint Bonaventure) was founded on March 31, 1782 by Fr. Junípero Serra. A first temporary chapel was set up, but a more permanent one was built that year. In 1787 foundation trenches for the present church were opened; in 1790 the walls proved to be out of plumb and had to be taken down. In 1791 the church then in use was burned, and in 1792 a temporary chapel was built. In 1793 work had begun on the new church; by 1799 the sacristy was completed. Finally, in 1809 it was well enough along to be blessed, though work continued, particularly in the completion of an arched ceiling. The roof above this was an *azotea* or terrace roof.

In 1812 there were three severe earthquakes which seriously damaged almost all of the buildings of the mission. The upper part of the church façade fell out of plumb and a large crack appeared in the wall behind the altar, enough to need rebuilding. The rest of the church appeared repairable, though the tower was so badly damaged that it was decided to tear it down. For more than two years work continued on the repairs, and in 1814 all the timbers had been replaced and a tile roof substituted for the *azotea*. The demolished tower was rebuilt and on July 4, 1815 the church was again in use. The church was stabilized by a buttress on the left side of the façade and a tower base overlapping the right side. Since the side of the church slopes down toward the sea some sort of support would have been required eventually, even without an earthquake.

In the early American period the mission became a central element in the new town which grew up around it, and the church continued as a parish church though the adjoining mission buildings were all eventually torn down. Shingles replaced the tiles after an earthquake in 1857, and the windows had been lengthened downward by 1870. The interior was seriously modified and modernized in the 1880s and 1890s.

Symbols of San Buenaventura

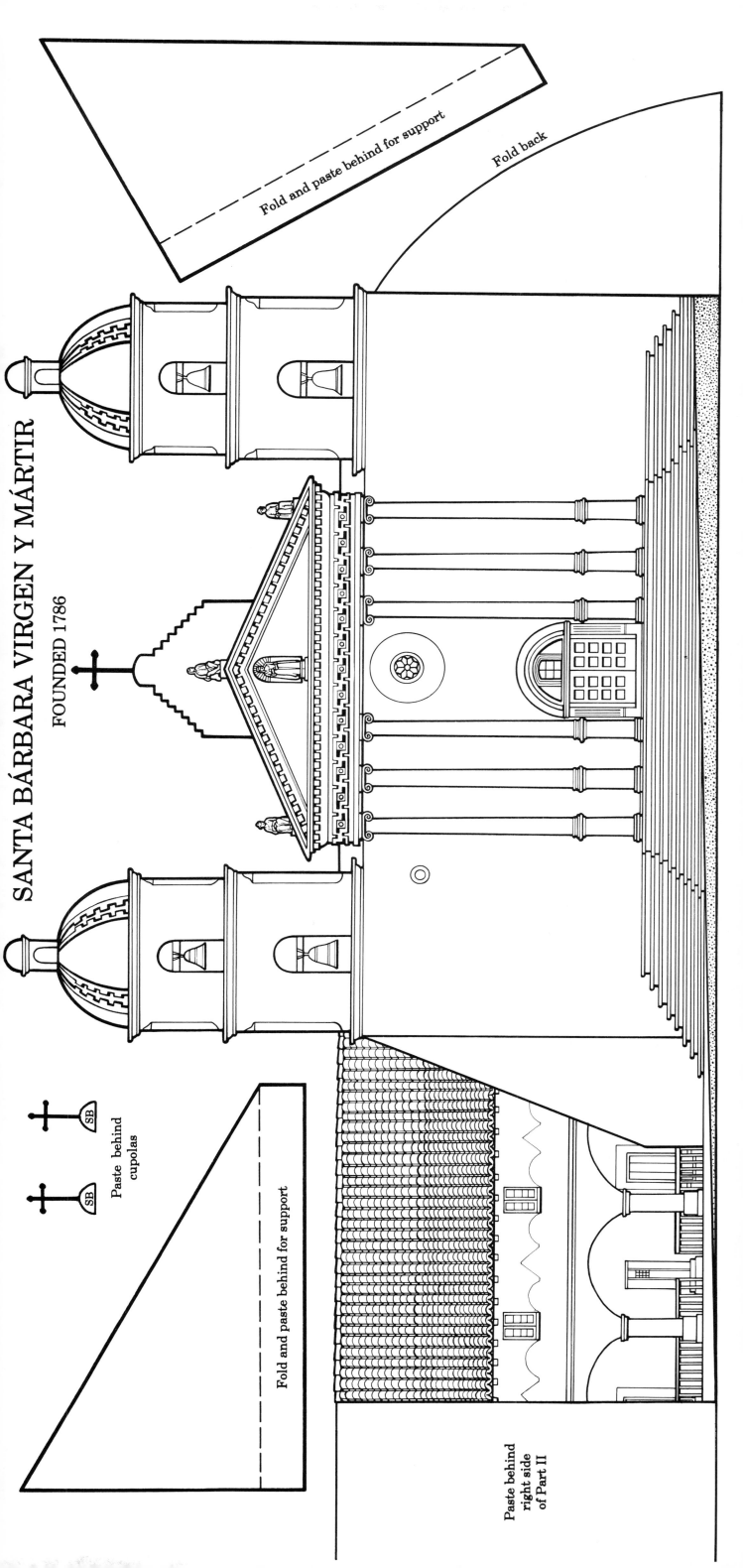

SANTA BÁRBARA VIRGEN Y MÁRTIR

FOUNDED 1786

Fold and paste behind for support

Fold back

Paste behind cupolas

Fold and paste behind for support

SB

SB

Paste behind right side of Part II

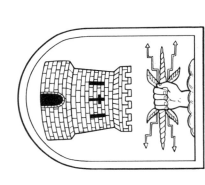

SANTA BÁRBARA VIRGEN Y MÁRTIR

California's tenth mission, dedicated to Santa Bárbara Virgen y Mártir (Saint Barbara Virgin and Martyr) was founded December 4, 1786 by Fr. Francisco Fermín de Lasuén four and half years after Serra had founded the presidio under the same patron. Mass, as usual, was said under a simple brush *enramada*. The first structures built the following year, including the chapel, were of upright poles plastered with mud and roofed with thatch. The chapel was 12 *varas* long and 3 wide. The following year it was lengthened and a tile roof was added. The first adobe church, built in 1789, was 30 *varas* long and 6 wide, and the roof was tiled. A second adobe church with its roof of tile was built in 1793-94; it was 45 *varas* long and 9¼ wide with a sacristy behind for another 5 *varas*. It was plastered inside and out and had a brick portico in front. Although not mentioned in the original description there were six side chapels 4 *varas* wide and 5 wide; six paintings for

them were received in 1791. In 1811 a new façade was begun. By then the fathers' dwelling had been completed with its stone arcade.

On December 21, 1812 a severe earthquake damaged the church, and although temporary repairs were made it became necessary to build a new church which was constructed from 1815 to 1820 around the existing structure. This was an unusual solution, possibly unique in California but not unknown elsewhere. This, the present church, is built of sandstone with walls 2 *varas* thick. It is 63 *varas* long and 10 wide with the original sacristy jutting out into the quadrangle. It has a tile roof. There are seven windows in the side walls and doors to the patio and to the cemetery. Above the exterior of the door to the cemetery was a carved skull and crossbones flanked by two real skulls; these have been replaced by casts. There are two side chapels near the choir

Santa Bárbara, Part II

Paste over tab on Part I

Fold
and
paste
Behind
for
support

Fold
and
paste
behind
for
support

Fold
and
paste
behind
for
support

Fold back

loft; one was originally used as a baptistry. The floor was of polished cement and the ceiling plastered and decorated with painted wooden appliqués. Six pairs of pilasters with Ionic capitals articulate the interior walls.

The central part of the façade is in the form of a hexastyle Ionic temple based on a plate in the 1787 Spanish edition of Vitruvius's *Ten Books of Architecture*. Decorative details on the plaster ceiling are from the same book. The central intercolumnation is widened to give space for the arched doorway and round window above. The pediment contains a niche with the statue of the patroness while the extremities and the summit of the pediment have statues of Faith, Hope, and Charity. The original statues (minus Faith, which was lost during the Mexican era) are now in the mission museum; they were originally painted with oil paints. They have been replaced by modern statues of the same subjects.

A stepped gable above and behind the pediment serves as a pedestal for the cross, but in the middle of the last century it held a clock surrounded by rays. The façade is flanked by twin belltowers, each of two levels topped by a dome. The first was completed in 1820 and the second in 1831. It collapsed and had to be rebuilt in 1833; the buttress to the side of it probably dates from this period. The towers and upper part of the façade were severely damaged in the 1925 earthquake, but the reconstruction was technically defective and the whole façade had to be taken down and rebuilt between 1950 and 1952.

This temple façade of the church is very typical of the international fashion of neoclassicism. Numerous churches in the Western World built at that time use a variation of the scheme of temple façade between twin towers. It is California's first example of "period" architecture!

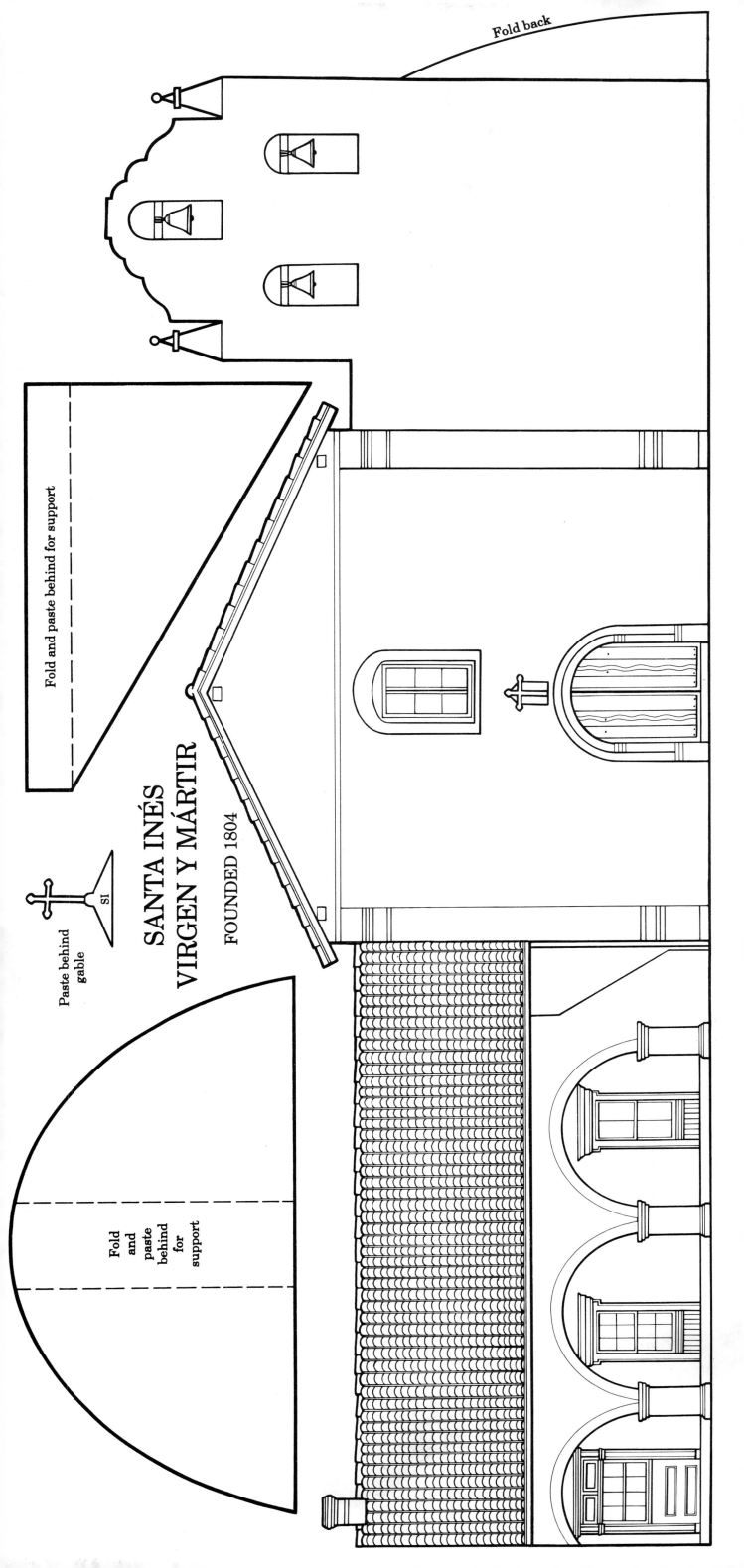

Fold back

Fold and paste behind for support

SANTA INÉS
VIRGEN Y MÁRTIR

FOUNDED 1804

Paste behind
gable

SI

Fold
and
paste
behind
for
support

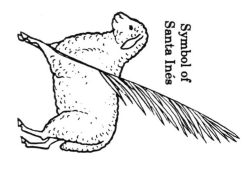

SANTA INÉS VIRGEN Y MÁRTIR

California's nineteenth mission, dedicated to Santa Inés Virgen y Mártir (Saint Agnes Virgin and Martyr) was founded on September 17, 1804 by the president of the missions Fr. Estevan Tapis. It was the last mission to be properly founded under orders from the Spanish viceroy in Mexico City. As with the preceding five missions it was founded to fill a gap in the chain. Work on an adobe church had already been started by the time of the foundation, but an enramada was used for the first Mass. The temporary church, 31 varas long and 7 wide with a sacristy for an additional 5 varas formed part of a structure 84 varas in length. This structure was damaged in the 1812 earthquake. An interim church was built in 1813; it was 45½ varas long and 7¼ wide with stone buttresses and a tile roof. It was located near the Indian village and later was used as a warehouse. In 1814 foundation trenches were opened for the final church, possibly on the site of the first one. Its dimensions are 50 varas long, 9 wide with adobe walls 2 varas thick and a brick facing on the façade. The sacristy adds 6 more varas to the length, and the roof is of tile. In 1817 it was blessed and a brick espadaña and buttresses were added. There are four windows on the cemetery side and three on the side toward the quadrangle, plus an additional one for the sacristy. Originally there were side doors both to the quadrangle and to the cemetery, but the

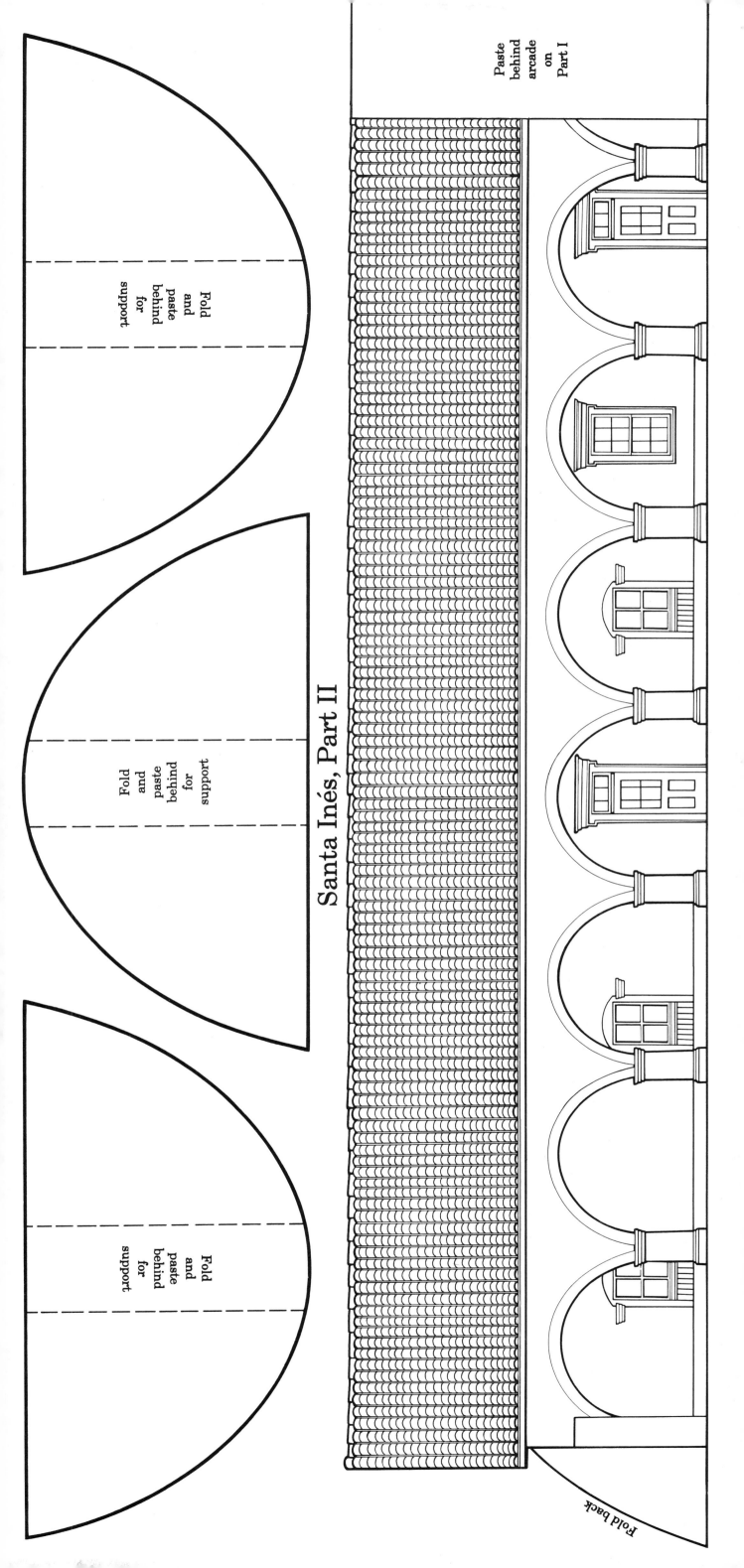

Santa Inés, Part II

Fold and paste behind for support

Fold and paste behind for support

Fold and paste behind for support

Paste behind arcade on Part I

Fold back

latter was blocked in at the end of the last century, and there is now a shrine inside. Another blocked doorway used as a shrine on the same side near the choir may have given access to a long-demolished baptistry, though a recess under the choir loft now fills that function. A door opposite it giving access to the mission museum was cut through some decades ago and is not original.

The brick façade, with its flat pilasters at the side and a connecting molding across the top, is a simplified classical temple design. The arched doorway has an inset relief cross above it. The large choir window is almost as large as the door below. The pilasters, cornice, and door frame were all ex-

ecuted in red cement, though this has been covered in a recent repainting. The belfry to the right is an *espadaña* with two bell arches below a single arch under an undulating gable flanked by pyramidal finials. The original structure collapsed in a storm in 1911 and was incorrectly restored in 1912 with an extra arch between the lower two arches in the end wall. This, in turn, was taken down in 1947 and rebuilt in the original form. About the same time the upper part of the fathers' dwelling was returned to its pre-1812 form with a terrace above the arcade and a second story. In 1990 this wing was also reconstructed to its original length.

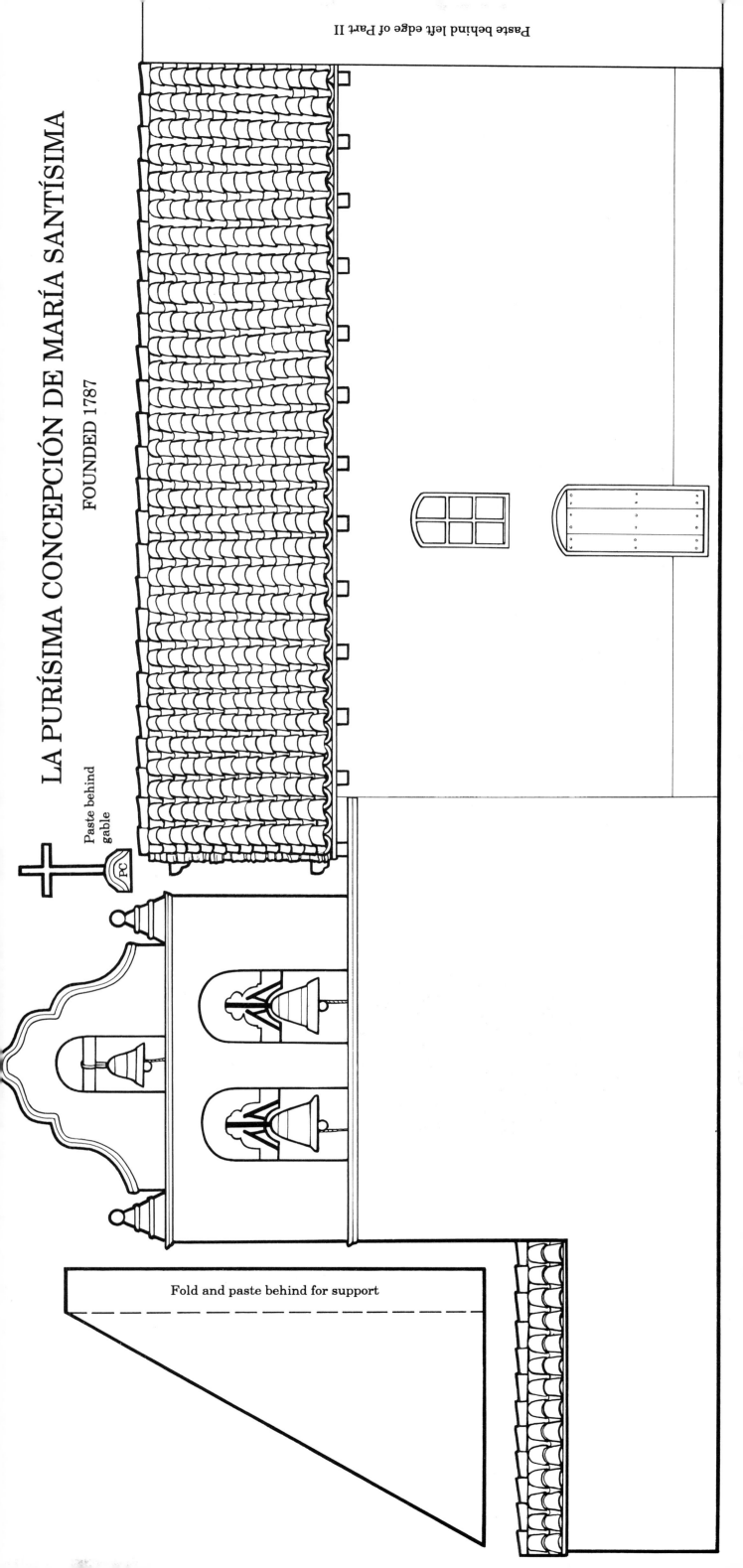

LA PURÍSIMA CONCEPCIÓN DE MARÍA SANTÍSIMA

FOUNDED 1787

Paste behind gable

PC

Paste behind left edge of Part II

Fold and paste behind for support

covered with adobes. In 1815 the great building containing the missionaries' quarters was erected; it included a private chapel. In 1817 foundations were prepared for a new church while the temporary one was repaired. In 1818 the church of *horconería* collapsed, and another temporary one was built nearby, probably the one begun the previous year. It was of adobe with a tile roof with a loft and sacristy and counter-sacristy. In 1821 a belltower and sacristy were added to this. Among the California missions the design of the church is unique. It has no entrance on its main axis and thus no proper façade. Because of the way the mission buildings were lined up there was no place for a façade. In fact, there was a spring under one corner of where the façade would be and this weakened the structure enough that services were transferred to the chapel in the fathers' dwelling which had been enlarged. The ceiling was raised so that a choir loft could be included, a detail not necessary when it was only a private chapel. Still, as late as 1835 the building of another church was being considered, perhaps at the far end of the fathers' dwelling, though there is no evidence that it was ever more than thought about.

Emblem of La Purísima
Concepción de María Santísima

La Purísima Concepción de María Santísima, Part II

LA PURÍSIMA CONCEPCIÓN
DE MARÍA SANTÍSIMA

The eleventh mission, dedicated to La Purísima Concepción de María Santísima (The Immaculate Conception of Mary Most Holy) was founded on December 8, 1787 at a site on the southern edge of the modern city of Lompoc. Heavy rains forced the missionaries to wait till the following spring to start the mission. Temporary structures of poles with roofs of straw were quickly erected and served until they could be replaced by ones of adobe. The first permanent church, built in 1789, was of adobe with a flat roof covered with straw and earth. It was 22 *varas* long and 6 wide; the sacristy added 5 *varas* to the length of this with the same width. In 1795 collection of materials for a more permanent church began, and the foundations for it were laid in 1798. The records do not give the dimensions, but recent investigations on the site show the exterior dimensions (records usually give the interior ones, however) were 54½ feet wide and 179 feet long; a reredos that came in 1810 that was over thirty feet high suggests that the height must have exceeded that. These dimensions suggest a very wide and rather squat proportion for the façade. The span exceeded the

Emblem of La Purísima
Concepción de María Santísima

length of then available lumber so there may have been posts or columns dividing the interior into nave and aisles or some sort of polygonal ceiling. An excavation of the church floor might resolve this question. The church was finished in 1803. Two fragmentary walls, flanking the main entrance, show that the façade had been partially of stone in its lower level and was covered with lime plaster. A projecting cornice of brick, whitewashed and then painted red, ran across the façade above the arch of the entrance door.

This church was completely ruined, along with much of the rest of the mission, by a severe earthquake on December 21, 1812. A temporary church of poles was put up, but it was soon realized that the site would have to be abandoned rather than rebuilt as the neophytes were unwilling to stay there. The following year the mission was transferred to the present site, some five leagues from the original. This was the only mission that changed its site at its peak.

The first church at the new site was of *horconería*, that is, forked poles

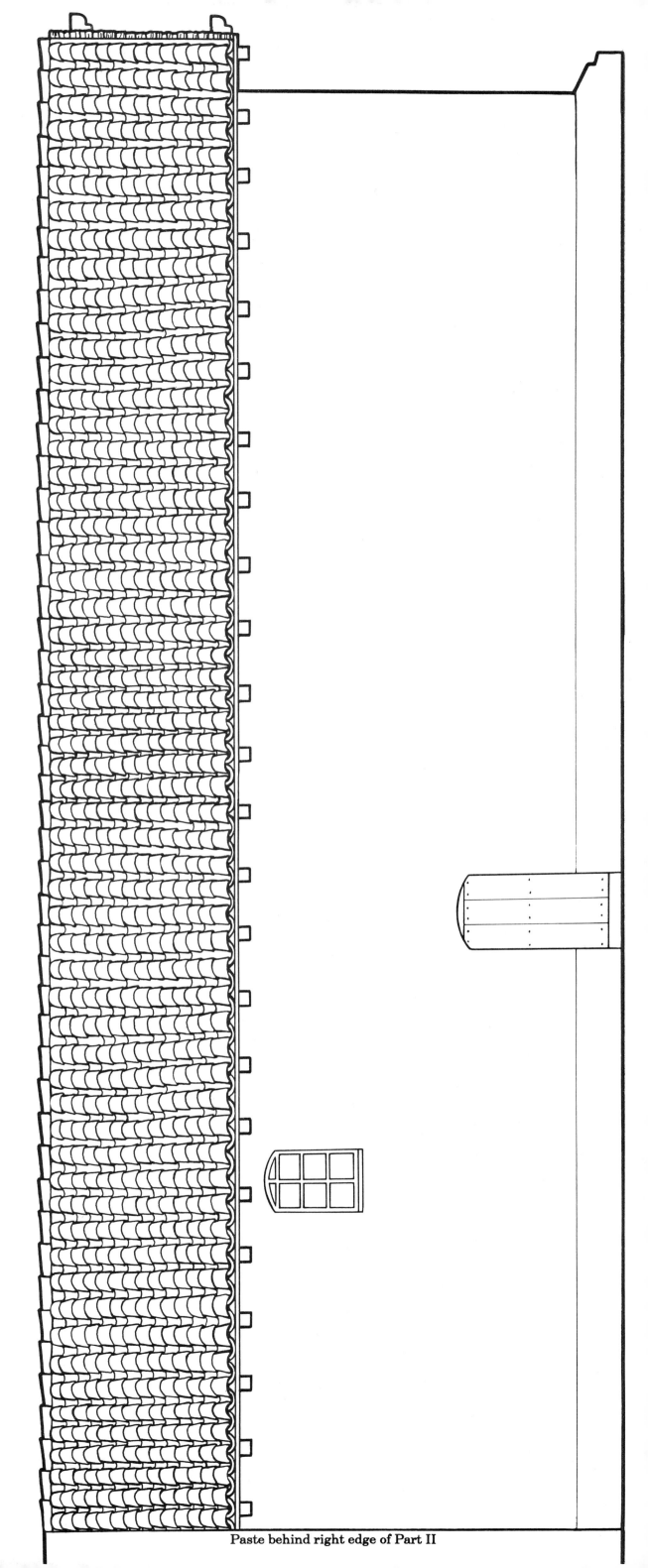

La Purísima Concepción de María Santísima, Part III

The Destruction by Earthquake of Old Mission La Purísima Concepción in 1812 and the moving of the Mission to the present site, from *Writings of Mariano Payeras* translated by Donald C. Cutter, and published by **Bellerophon Books**, Santa Barbara

. . . The extraordinary and dreadful earthquake which this mission suffered on the memorable day of the glorious Apostle Santo Tomás, ruined the church completely; destroyed the altar, various images, and paintings and ruined the greater part of its furnishings. The vestments were not destroyed because they were inside the drawers. Some of its buildings have collapsed, but others, if the damage does not continue, might be restored to use after thorough repair, not as living quarters, but rather for minor uses which do not require as much security.

A hundred neophytes' houses and the pozole building, which were all made of adobe and mortar and roofed with tile, are useless. Even the orchard's adobe wall, which is covered with tile, is either collapsed or leaning so that the damaged parts will scarcely provide any material for the one that later on must be built.

The goods and equipment of the mission have also suffered; some are flattened, others destroyed, and all are damaged without taking into consideration the bad weather and heavy rains which immediately came without permitting opportunity to dig things up, or to re-roof what barely remained standing.

The most necessary items were dug out quickly, and what is most urgent has been fixed. A large Indian hut has been made over into a church, and two huts are serving as primitive lodging for the priests. We will continue to build the essential buildings out of wood and grass until the earth quiets down and experience shows us the most proper methods for the later buildings. This is the true status of this Mission of La Purísima.

31 December 1812

. . . To see what damage had been done, we inspected the interior of the storehouses and we found sadly that all of them are useless from foundation to roof; that the church is destroyed completely; and that neither priests, nor soldiers, nor neophytes want to, nor can, live without fear and

danger in their partly collapsed, partly leaning, and completely cracked quarters. The time has come to employ a thousand and more willing persons. But our suffering is not lessened by knowing that to rebuild in this location, which is limited by what is already built, we must first tear down with obvious danger what has remained standing, clear off debris, and dig up even the foundations, which, like the buildings, are cracked. Then we must begin again to build in such a badly situated and defective location. May the most skilled builders consider seriously this critical situation!

This miserable state of affairs, and especially contemplating the great amount of work which the neophytes would have to endure as a consequence of the proposed plan, far from frightening us, it moved us to consider a more favorable and happier idea; namely, to look for a place where, with the consent of Your Lordship, we may construct without obstruction a medium-sized but solid and strong mission with the advantage of not losing a single brick or tile from the old [mission], by transporting them on muleback and in carts.

Having considered everything, the place which we consider as best is the location of Los Berros, on the other side of the river, 1¼ leagues to the northeast of the present buildings. Because carrying out the planned transfer not only concerns us, but also involves the corporal of the *escolta*, Vicente Villa, and the approval of all the neophytes, we have already thought it over and have placed outlines at the aforementioned place of all that a mission needs. . .

. . . Because the mission that Your Reverence and our deceased superior [Lasuén] founded was destroyed, we have reestablished it at Los Berros. The advantages are well-known, especially in the matter of climate, and include the great benefit that the river brings water from the old site to this new one. Every little bit of what was still useable from the old mission, including tile and brick, etc., has been utilized. The distance from one place to the other by the most direct road is 1¼ leagues and the present site is located on the camino real in a pretty and clear place. The harvests are good, the fruit abundant, and now the vines on the beach are beginning to bear fruit.

31 September 1813